An introductic

Sempervivum
and
Jovibarba
Species and Cultivars

Written and Published
by
Howard and Sally Wills

First published in Great Britain in 2004 by Howard and Sally Wills.

ISBN 0-9547533-0-5

© Howard and Sally Wills 2004

Website: www.fernwood-nursery.co.uk
E-mail: hw@fernwood-nursery.co.uk

All photographs by Howard Wills or Sally Wills

Front Cover and Title Page - Mixed groups of *Sempervivum* species and cultivars.

Sempervivum 'Lively Bug'

How my interest started

Back in the 1950s a Great Aunt of mine had a conservatory on the side of her house in which she grew a small collection of cacti and other succulents. One of her plants she called 'The Cobweb Cactus'. This little plant was covered in a dense mass of cobweb-like hairs and produced many baby plants that hung over the edge of the pot. I can remember being delighted when she gave me some of these offsets to take home and grow for myself. Later, I learnt that this plant was actually *Sempervivum arachnoideum,* not a cactus at all, and that it was fully hardy. I also discovered that there were many other beautiful sempervivums that could be grown without needing a greenhouse. From then on, I was hooked...

Howard Wills

Contents

Sempervivum ciliosum subsp. *octopodes*

Sempervivum 'The Flintstones'

Sempervivum 'Banyan'

Jovibarba heuffelii 'Symphony'

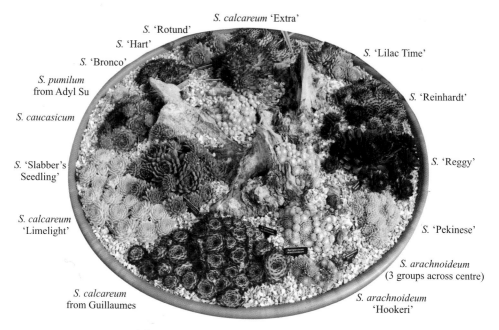

S. calcareum 'Extra'

S. 'Rotund'

S. 'Hart'

S. 'Bronco'

S. pumilum
from Adyl Su

S. caucasicum

S. 'Slabber's
Seedling'

S. calcareum
'Limelight'

S. 'Lilac Time'

S. 'Reinhardt'

S. 'Reggy'

S. 'Pekinese'

S. arachnoideum
(3 groups across centre)

S. calcareum
from Guillaumes

S. arachnoideum
'Hookeri'

A large bowl planted with sempervivums

Sempervivums on an old tree stump

| Sempervivum arachnoideum | Sempervivum 'Westerlin' | Sempervivum atlanticum | Sempervivum 'Atropurpureum' |

Sempervivum calcareum

Sempervivum and Jovibarba

Introduction

Members of the genus *Sempervivum* are alpine plants belonging to the family *Crassulaceae*. They are commonly known as '**Houseleeks**' or '**Hen and Chickens**'.

Sempervivums grow naturally in mountain areas ranging from the Atlas Mountains of Morocco, across the whole of Central Europe, through the Balkans, Caucasus and into Iran. There are no species native to Great Britain although there are a few instances where garden escapes have naturalized, but probably only temporarily.

The genus *Jovibarba* is closely related to *Sempervivum,* and in fact, some authorities consider that it is too similar to warrant separate generic status. The main feature that distinguishes the two genera is flower structure.

Sempervivum flowers are open, with 10-15 narrow and widely spreading petals. The most common colours are shades of red, pink and purple, often with a darker central stripe. There are also a number of species that have yellow or cream petals.

Sempervivum altum

Sempevivum marmoreum subsp. *reginae-amaliae*

Sempervivum ciliosum

Jovibarba flowers have fewer petals, (normally 5-7) and these are joined together at the base. The flower itself is cup shaped rather than open. The petals are normally yellow but this can shade from almost white to a much stronger, creamy yellow colour.

Jovibarba hirta

Jovibarba heuffelii

Typically, the rosettes of *Sempervivum* produce **offsets** (young plantlets) on **stolons** (side stems) that may be long or short but which are relatively substantial, and firmly attached to the parent plant. In *Jovibarba* the stolons are either non-existent (*Jovibarba heuffelii*) or very fragile so that the young plantlets (called '**rollers**') detach easily from the parent plant.

Although the form of the vegetative rosettes is quite similar in both types, there is never any doubt about identification when the plants are in flower. For this reason, we prefer to keep the two genera separate, but we will use the word 'sempervivums' (not italicised) as a general term applying to both *Sempervivum* and *Jovibarba.* (Genus names should always be printed in *italics.*)

Sempervivum history

Houseleeks have traditionally been grown on European roofs since the Middle Ages. They were believed to protect buildings against lightening and thunderbolts. The Roman Emperor, Charlemagne (A.D. 768-814) actually decreed that all of the buildings in his possession should have houseleeks planted on them.

Houseleeks were first cultivated in Britain for their supposed herbal properties. In **Culpeper's Herbal** of 1652 it is stated that they "*grow commonly upon walls and house-sides*" and "*are so well known to my countrymen, that I shall not need to write any description of them.*" This is followed by an impressive list of ailments that could be treated with the leaf juices.

> "Our ordinary Houseleek is good for all inward heats as well as outward, and in the eyes or other parts of the body; a posset made with the juice of Houseleek, is singularly good in all hot agues, for it cools and tempers the blood and spirits, and quenches the thirst; and also good to stay all hot defluctions or sharp and salt rheums in the eyes, the juice being dropped into them, or into the ears. It helps also other fluxes of humours in the bowels, and the immoderate courses of women. It cools and restrains all other hot inflammations, St. Anthony's fire, scaldings and burnings, the shingles, fretting ulcers, cankers, tetters, ringworms, and the like; and much eases the pains of the gout proceeding from any hot cause. The juice also takes away warts and corns in the hands or feet, being often bathed therewith, and the skin and leaves being laid on them afterwards. It eases also the head-ache, and distempered heat of the brain in frenzies, or through want of sleep, being applied to the temples and forehead. The leaves bruised and laid upon the crown or seam of the head stays bleeding at the nose very quickly. The distilled water of the herb is profitable for all the purposes aforesaid. The leaves being gently rubbed on any place stung with nettles or bees, doth quickly take away the pain."

The juice from sempervivum leaves is probably harmless and may have a soothing effect on the skin as it evaporates and cools. There is, even today, a commonly held belief that extracts of sempervivum leaves can be used to treat earache, some skin conditions and various other ailments. Unfortunately, there is little or no scientific evidence to support these claims.

In 1753 Linnaeus gave the Common Houseleek its scientific name *Sempervivum tectorum.* (*Sempervivum* = 'always alive', *tectorum* = 'from the roofs'.) He also named four other species known at that time, *S. arachnoideum* (The Cobweb Houseleek), *S. montanum* (The Mountain Houseleek), *S. globiferum* and *S. hirtum*.

The last two species were later separated from *Sempervivum* and placed in a new genus called *Jovibarba* (originally *Diopogon*). There is still a lot of debate about the best way of classifying these plants and opinions differ regarding the most appropriate use of the names.

The earliest recorded *Sempervivum* cultivars were named in the late 1800s: *S.* 'Violescens' (1868), *S.* 'Boissieri' (1879) and *S.* 'Triste' (1879). In the first half of the 20th century there was not a lot of interest in *Sempervivum* cultivars but various new species were collected from the European mountains and a number of new cultivars were named.

Sempervivum 'Boissieri'

However, it was not until the 1950s that enthusiasts began to actively produce and name new cultivars. Crosses between various species were carried out experimentally and seeds produced as a result of accidental pollination were collected and germinated. No doubt the occasional mutations occurred giving rise to interesting variants. The best of the new forms were selected and cultivated and over the next few decades hundreds of cultivars were named.

During this time sempervivums were not particularly admired by most gardeners. Cactus and succulent enthusiasts tended to overlook them because they did not require the careful treatment and greenhouse cultivation that other succulents need. Alpine gardeners usually preferred the small, brightly flowered types of plants, which again often required special care, or even the protection of an alpine house. However, a small number of enthusiasts continued to grow and develop new and ever more beautiful cultivars.

In 1970 **The Sempervivum Society** was set up in Great Britain, and for the next 20 years its journals and newsletters were instrumental in spreading information and stimulating interest in this group of plants. Sempervivums were still very much a minority interest but by the end of the 20th century, there were nearly four thousand named cultivars. The Sempervivum Society ceased activity in the mid 1990s but the production of cultivars has continued unabated. Each year hundreds of new ones are named by a small number of enthusiasts from all over the world.

Over the last few years, there has been an increasing interest in sempervivums by the gardening fraternity. People are beginning to appreciate the colourful displays that can be produced in places that are often inhospitable for other plants. Their ease of care and their tolerance of neglect makes them ideal for those who have little time to spare, or who are away from home for long periods.

Common names

The name '**Houseleek**' originally applied only to *Sempervivum tectorum* but it now tends to be used as a general name for all species of *Sempervivum,* sometimes prefixed with a qualifier such as '**Cobweb**' or '**Mountain**'. It is also commonly used for *Jovibarba* species although a more accurate name for these is '**Jove's Beard**' - a literal translation of the genus name.

Jovibarba sobolifera

The descriptive name '**Hen and Chickens**' is often used by American collectors and is becoming well known here as well. It seems particularly appropriate for the *Jovibarba* species that produce many ball-like offsets that roll off the parent plant and cluster around it.

Other common names for sempervivums include '**Live-for-ever**', '**Sengreen**', '**Thunderleek**' and various versions of what is said to be the longest common name of any plant - '**Welcome home husband however drunk you may be**'.

3

Plant structure

Leaves

The main attraction of sempervivums is their colourful rosettes of leaves. These range from bright yellow, through various shades of green, grey, pink, purple, red, orange and brown, to almost black in some varieties. The colour may be the same all over the leaf or it may shade from one colour to another from base to tip or from center to sides.

'Cmiral's Yellow'   'Silver Thaw'   'Graupurpur'   'Twilight Blues'   'Bernstein'

There are no truly variegated varieties but many show mottled colours or bands of shading and occasionally pale stripes. The leaf tips are often distinctly darker or lighter than other parts and sometimes this colour extends along the edges of the leaves to give an attractive outline to the leaf. The leaf margins are often fringed with small silver hairs (cilia) that also emphasize the outline. The leaf surface may be dull or glossy, or covered with a velvety pubescence or longer hairs. The leaf shape can vary from short, almost round, to long, tapering, and finely pointed.

In some varieties, the leaf tips bear a tuft of longer hairs that connect the tips together. As the leaves grow, these hairs elongate to form a 'cobweb' over the surface of the rosettes. In their natural habitat, this may help to protect the rosettes from scorching or from desiccation. The cobweb normally disappears in the winter but forms again when light levels increase in the spring.

S. arachnoideum

The colour and form of the leaves can also show remarkable changes through the year. Many are at their brightest during the spring and summer although there are a number of cultivars that show their best colour in the autumn or winter. The type of soil, the weather conditions, and the age of the individual rosette all combine to affect the appearance in ways that are often unpredictable. Many plants will turn green in the winter or if grown in poor light.

Sempervivum 'Gallivarda' at different times of the year

March   July   September   November

It is the endless range of different leaf shapes, colours and textures that make this group so interesting to enthusiasts. Looking at sempervivums, it is easy to imagine that the rosettes are flowers rather than just coloured leaves.

Stems

In the non-flowering state, the stem of a sempervivum plant is usually so short that it is invisible and the plant appears as a rosette of leaves at ground level. Occasionally, older plants will elongate so that a short stem becomes apparent but this is unusual.

Sempervivums reproduce vegetatively by means of **offsets** (baby plants) on lateral stems called **stolons**. These arise from the axils of the lower leaves of a rosette and usually have scale leaves of their own. In some varieties the stolons are very short and only visible when a rosette is pulled from a parent plant. More commonly the stolons are long enough to send the offsets a few centimeters from the parent but in some species they can be 20 cm or more long.

Sempervivum ciliosum subsp. *octopodes*

Sempervivum reginae-amaliae var. *erythraeum*

Sempervivum ciliosum subsp. *ciliosum*

Sempervivum charadzeae

S. 'Blue Boy' (offset)

Roots

Sempervivums can survive in very little soil and in the wild, they sometimes appear to be growing on the surface of bare rock. However, they do have extensive root systems that can penetrate down between cracks in the rock to obtain water, nutrients and anchorage.

There may be one or more fleshy main roots and these then produce large numbers of smaller branches. The fleshy roots probably act as a reserve of food and water as well as providing anchorage.

Despite having extensive root systems the rosettes do not appear to suffer much if their roots are damaged or removed. They readily grow new roots from the base of the rosette.

Sempervivum calcareum

Flowers

Sempervivums are **monocarpic**, which means that they only flower once and then die. In their second or third year, many rosettes will stop producing offsets and begin the process of flowering. The first sign of this is usually a deepening of colour of a large rosette, followed by elongation of the main stem. This grows upwards for 10 to 30 cm then produces a large cluster of attractive flowers. The most common flower colours are shades of pink, purple or red but some species have yellow or cream flowers. The flowers are star-shaped with 8 to 16, widely spreading petals.

Sempervivum 'Starburst'
Stem elongating prior to flowering

Sempervivum 'Starburst'
Flower buds

S. 'Dyke'

A succession of individual flowers is produced on each flowering stem over a period of many weeks.

Sempervivum 'Excalibur' - Flower buds

Sempervivum flowers are pollinated by insects and most will produce fertile seed. The seeds are very small and are probably dispersed by wind. The whole flower head will eventually detach from the ground and get blown away, dispersing any remaining seeds as it goes.

As the old flowers die off and set seed the whole inflorescence can begin to look rather untidy. Some people choose to cut off the flower stalk at this stage although this does not help the plant at all.

Sempervivum calcareum from Guillaumes

Sempervivums are normally grown for their leaves rather than their flowers. This is not because the flowers are insignificant, but the rosettes of leaves are so colourful that flowers are just an extra bonus. The fact that flowering marks the end of the life of an individual rosette can also add a slight feeling of disappointment.

However, the flowers are well worth examining in detail. There is a wide range of variation in shape, size and colour and they are very attractive to bees and other insects.

S. calcareum
'Sir Wm. Lawrence'

Sempervivum 'Kramer's Spinrad'

S. 'Shirley Moore'

S. 'Proud Zelda'

A selection of Sempervivum flowers

S. 'Purdy's 90-1'

S. 'Yvette'

S. tectorum
var. boutignianum

S. arachnoideum
var. tomentosum

S. arachnoideum 'Album'

J. heuffelii 'Tan'

Initiation of flowering

It is usually possible to tell at an early stage that a rosette is going to flower. Normally it is larger than the non-flowering rosettes, the colours become more intense, the leaves in the centre of the rosette become more upright. The centre of the rosette then begins to elongate upwards to form the flowering stem. All of these features can be seen in the photograph on the right. The central rosette is at an early stage and the upper rosette is beginning to elongate.

Various factors determine whether a particular rosette will produce offsets or flowers. It is unusual for a rosette to flower in its first year but as a general rule it is unlikely to go on producing offsets for more than two or three years. Some varieties seem prone to flower at a young age while others appear reluctant to flower at all.

Sempervivum 'Butterbur'

Environmental factors also play a significant role in determining flowering. As with many other plants, adverse conditions that cause some form of stress, appear to stimulate flowering. In sempervivums, it is thought that stress such as dehydration in the autumn or in the early spring, increases the chances of flowering the following summer.

Annual growth cycle

Through the winter, sempervivums are practically dormant but as the days lengthen and temperature rises in the spring they start to grow again. The first signs of new growth often appear in late February, and by April most are growing well and some may be starting to produce offsets.

The growth patterns are very dependent on the weather conditions but probably it is day-length that has the main determining effect. Obviously, factors such at temperature, water availability and nutrient levels can have a limiting effect on growth even if day-length is stimulating the plant to grow.

Through the summer, plants grow rapidly and usually produce one or more sets of offsets. These put down roots and soon become established as individual plants. The connection to the parent plant usually remains until either the old plant flowers and dies, or until the physical growth of the offset actually pushes it away from the parent and breaks the connection.

Rosettes that are about to flower do not produce offsets but instead begin elongating upwards eventually forming a many-flowered inflorescence. Flower production is greatest during the summer from June to August, but some start earlier and some continue to develop flowers well into the autumn. Flowering stems that start to form late in the year often do not elongate as they normally would and the flowers appear at rosette level.

Towards the end of the summer, growth of the vegetative rosettes begins to slow down. This may be followed by a period of slightly more rapid growth in the autumn as the plants prepare for their winter dormancy. There may be accumulation of food reserves in the roots at this time. By November, growth has just about ceased and the plants will remain dormant until the following spring.

Cultivation

Introduction

Sempervivums grow naturally in mountain regions where the environmental conditions can be extremely harsh. During the summer they will be exposed to very bright light and high temperatures in the daytime yet there may be sub-zero temperatures at night. Rainfall may be torrential, but water will drain away very quickly and the plants may have to withstand long periods of dehydration. In the winter, there will be long periods when sempervivums may be covered with snow and ice but under these conditions they will, in effect, be dry rather than wet, as any water will be frozen solid.

When cultivating plants in our gardens it is normal to try to mimic the conditions under which a plant grows in its natural habitat. We cannot duplicate the mountain heights but, since sempervivums are such tough plants and so well adapted to extremes of environmental conditions it is only necessary to avoid the few factors that they are not used to.

They will not thrive in shady conditions or where the soil remains waterlogged for long periods. However, as long as they have bright light and good drainage they will cope with most other conditions. The name '*Sempervivum*' means 'Always alive' (from the Latin: *semper* = always, and *vivus* = alive).

Growing in containers

Most enthusiasts grow sempervivums in pots or other containers. This allows the plants to be provided with a suitable soil and placed where they can be seen easily and where they can receive good levels of light. The size of pot is not critical but it must have good drainage holes.

Plants will survive in very little soil and in a small pot they will mound up and overhang the edges of the pot. Eventually they will need to be moved to a larger pot or split among several pots. They will, of course, grow better if they are given a reasonable depth of soil and room to spread but it is probably a mistake to start with too large a container. The soil in this case can become stale before the plant grows large enough to make use of it. It is better to start with a small container and then move the plant to a bigger one when it needs more space.

A collection of sempervivums in plastic pots

Most of the plants in the above photograph have been recently re-pottted into containers that are large enough to allow for a season's growth.

9

Provided that they have good drainage holes, stone troughs make ideal containers for mixed displays of sempervivums. Genuine stone troughs are getting hard to find and are usually very expensive. They are also very heavy and difficult to move. This can be an advantage once the trough is in position and there is no doubt that a genuine trough always looks and feels better than an imitation one.

A large granite trough planted with a variety of different sempervivums

White 'butler' sinks can be covered with hyper-tufa (a mixture of cement, sand and peat) to make them look more like stone.

It is also possible to buy modern concrete versions of stone troughs.

Plastic troughs made from a type of expanded resin are now for sale in many garden centres. These look very much like real stone but have hardly any of the weight.

A plastic 'stone trough' planted with sempervivums and other plants. Pieces of driftwood have been used to add interest.

Almost any type of container that will hold a small amount of soil can be used as a pot for sempervivums. For example: house bricks, screen walling blocks, pieces of driftwood, old kitchen utensils, tin cans, hanging baskets, shells, old boots, car tyres, and more conventional containers such as seed trays and bonsai pots. Even broken pots look good with a few sempervivums growing in them.

An engineering brick

An aquarium planter

Soil requirements

Sempervivums will grow in almost any type of soil provided that it is well drained. For growing in containers, a very suitable mixture is one consisting of approximately 50% multipurpose compost, (peat based or peat substitute), 25% loam (or John Innes No.1 or No.2) and about 25% coarse grit, to ensure good drainage.

Under natural conditions sempervivums often grow in very poor soil but their extensive root systems can penetrate deep into the ground to obtain nutrients. In containers, where there is usually a relatively restricted soil depth, they seem to grow best when provided with a good supply of nutrients. Slow-release fertiliser granules can be added to the compost at the rate recommended for alpine plants. (Usually about 3gm/litre of compost.) Alternatively, the plants can be given an occasional feed with a general purpose liquid fertiliser.

Plastic pots usually have a good number of drainage holes so it is not usually necessary to add crocks to the bottom of the pot. Terracotta pots and ceramic planters often have only a single drainage hole and this is sometimes not at the lowest point in the pot. A good layer of crocks or stones can help to prevent the hole from getting blocked.

A top dressing of coarse grit around the neck of each plant provides an attractive background and prevents the plant from being splashed with mud during heavy rain. It may also help to provide good drainage around the neck of the plant.

In large containers, the bottom of the container can be filled with lumps of expanded polystyrene packing to save on compost and to reduce weight.

Although sempervivums will continue growing for many years in the same soil they usually grow far better in fresh soil. After a few years, most plants will have

Sempervivum 'Madeleine'

produced a large number of offsets and there may be unsightly gaps in the clump where mature rosettes have flowered and died. It is a good idea to re-pot plants every year or two and, either detach some of the offsets for planting elsewhere, or spread them out so that they have more room to root and grow. Even plants growing in open ground benefit from being dug up, divided and re-planted occasionally.

Sempervivums are remarkably tolerant of root damage and in fact, they sometimes seem to grow better if most of the old roots are removed when re-potting.

Light

Sempervivums should be always be grown in good light. They are perfectly happy to be in full sun all day long if this is possible, but if not, then the more sun the better. Generally speaking, the brighter the light the better the colours of the rosettes. In shade, they soon turn green and the growth becomes soft and lax. They do not make good houseplants.

Water

In Great Britain it is hardly ever necessary to water plants grown outdoors. They usually receive more than enough from rainfall and it is generally more important to make sure that excess water can easily drain away than to provide it. If there is a long period of drought, especially in the spring and early summer when growth is most active, then a good soaking may encourage more rapid growth. If they remain dry at this time, growth may slow down and the rosettes may even begin to look slightly shriveled but they soon recover when wet weather returns.

In the winter, the problem is almost always one of too much water rather than too little. In their natural environment, precipitation would normally be in the form of snow rather than rain and any water would be frozen. Provided that drainage is good, most sempervivums will cope with our winter rain but if they end up sitting in cold waterlogged soil for long periods they can be prone to rotting off.

If this is a problem then any efforts made to deflect rainfall away from the plants will be beneficial. A simple transparent cover supported over the pots or a more elaborate cold frame will serve the purpose. The aim should be to reduce water without reducing ventilation or light levels. There is no need to try and keep the plants protected from the cold. In fact, the appearance of the rosettes when covered in frost can

Frosted rosette

be very attractive. It is not usually necessary to cover a collection but as a precaution, a few offsets of the more delicate varieties can be potted up and over-wintered in a cold frame or unheated greenhouse.

Staging for sempervivums

Sempervivums are relatively small and low-growing so it is usually a great benefit if their pots can be raised so that they can be viewed easily without having to bend down to ground level. This makes weeding, propagation, photography or other activities much easier and has the additional benefit of raising plants out of the reach of some ground-living pests. An elevated position also may provide better drainage.

Larger containers such as troughs can be raised on bricks or other purpose-made supports.

A simple, relatively inexpensive, and long-lasting staging for potted plants can be built from 100mm thick concrete blocks and 600mm square paving slabs. The arrangement of blocks shown in the picture below is very stable and the bench can be made longer or shorter if necessary. Lower level platforms can be made by leaving out the vertical blocks and using a slightly different arrangement of horizontal blocks. (See the photograph on Page 9)

This staging can be assembled without needing any cementing because the weight of the slabs holds the blocks in position. This means that it can easily be extended, moved to a new position or dismantled and the materials used for a different purpose.

Outdoor staging built with concrete blocks and paving slabs

Growing in the open garden

Sempervivums are ideal rockery plants. They are hardy, colourful and will grow into very attractive mounds of rosettes. The soil in most gardens is quite suitable for them although on heavy soils it may be necessary to add some grit for extra drainage. As well as mixing grit to the soil it is a good idea to spread a liberal layer on the surface and actually plant into this. The sempervivums will enjoy the good drainage around the rosettes and root down through the gravel into the soil below. They can also be planted in normal garden beds and borders provided that they get plenty of sunlight and are not shaded by larger plants.

Sempervivums and other plants in a garden bed

The traditional place for growing sempervivums is on roofs, but the edges of gravel paths and drives, spaces between paving slabs, the tops and sides of walls, and other rather inhospitable areas are places where sempervivums often thrive and where other, less tolerant plants may not.

Sempervivums growing on stone walls

13

Planting times

Sempervivums can be planted at almost any time of the year but in the winter they are dormant so are unlikely to start growing until the days lengthen in the spring. It is probably better to leave them undisturbed at this time of year because damage to the roots could result in infection leading to rotting off. If it is necessary to plant in the winter then it is advisable to keep the newly potted plants relatively dry until growth starts again in the spring.

There is some evidence that disturbing a plant late in the year or very early in the spring causes stress that can increase the chances of flowering. This is unlikely to be a problem with young rosettes but it is something to be taken into consideration when moving or splitting older groups of plants.

The best time to plant sempervivums in containers or in the garden, is in the spring or early summer. From late March onwards the plants are actively growing and the earlier they can get established in their new position the longer the growing season they have ahead of them.

Later in the summer, the current year's offsets are usually well grown and large enough to be taken away from the parent plant. This is a good time to plant up offsets in pots to grow on or to plant out the following year.

By the end of September, growth is slowing down and young offsets planted at this time, may not root before winter comes. They will usually survive the winter but they tend to get lifted by frost and need re-planting in the spring.

A newly planted trough - April

The photograph on the left shows an artificial stone trough on the day that it was planted in early April.

The photograph below shows the same trough as it appeared four months later, in August.

In most cases the same plants can be distinguished in each photograph.

The technique of planting a wide range of different varieties and allowing them to grow together, results in a fascinating display that gradually changes through the seasons.

It has the disadvantage that it is difficult to label the plants without spoiling the effect.

The same trough four months later - August

14

Other planting ideas

Sempervivums are available in a wide range of colours and their neat growth patterns make them ideal for small carpet bedding plantings. They also lend themselves to various ornamental or geometrical planting designs.

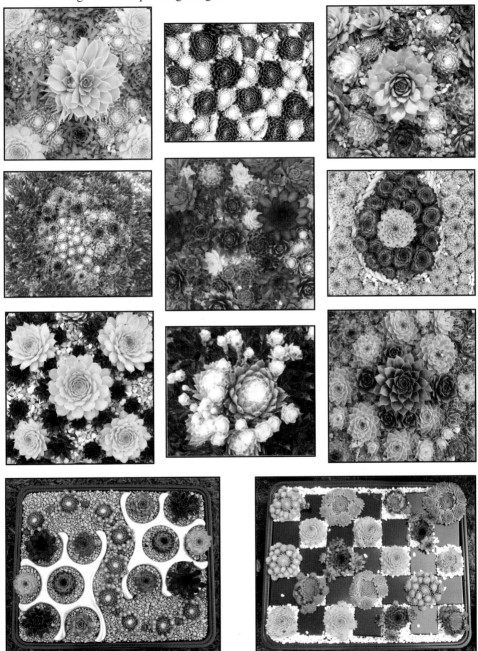

Propagation

Propagation from offsets

Soon after the end of winter dormancy, *Sempervivum* rosettes normally start to produce offsets (baby plants) on the ends of special lateral stems called **stolons.** Each of the offsets will send down roots of their own and eventually become detached from the parent rosette when the stolon withers, or when the parent plant dies after flowering.

Sempervivum 'Jewel Case'

Once they have started to root, the young offsets can be detached from the parent rosette and planted up separately. When an offset is pulled away from the parent plant, the stolon usually breaks quite easily at the end close to the parent, leaving a length of stolon attached to the offset. When planting the young offsets, it is probably best to break off the stolon close to the base of the young plant. The roots then develop from the offset itself rather than from the end of the stolon.

The number of offsets produced varies with different plants. Some may produce large numbers and keep producing new ones throughout the spring and summer. Others may only produce one or two in a year.

The number of offsets produced will also depend on the growing conditions. Under good conditions, vegetative growth is favoured and rosettes will produce offsets rather than flowers.

Sempervivum 'Zenith'

Sempervivum 'Waterlily'

The attractive cultivar *Sempervivum* 'Waterlily' (Left) produces very few offsets.

Sempervivum arachnoideum (Right) may produce two lots of offsets in a year.

Sempervivum arachnoideum

Since they are produced vegetatively, the offsets are genetically identical to their parent rosette. By propagating from offsets, the inherited characteristics of the parent are preserved. This is the only way of producing more plants of a named cultivar.

Growing from seed

Most flowering rosettes produce fertile seeds, and seedlings can often be found growing around the adult plants. However, hybridization is very common so the resultant offspring will not be the same as the parent.

Many enthusiasts like to grow plants from seed, either to experiment with the results of crossing different varieties, or in the hopes of developing new and attractive cultivars.

Sempervivum seed heads

Large numbers of seeds can be collected in the autumn by shaking the mature seed heads over a piece of paper or into a plastic container. The seeds can be sown immediately and left to over-winter in the soil but it is probably better to store them in a cool dry place then sow them the following spring.

In March or April the seeds should be scattered very lightly over the surface of sterilized seed compost then covered with a very thin sprinkling of sand. They can be left outside and will normally germinate within a few weeks.

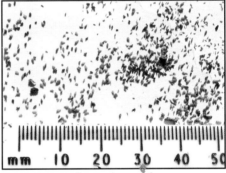

Sempervivum seeds

Sempervivum seedlings

The first sign of germination is the appearance of a pair of tiny succulent seed leaves (cotyledons) and this is soon followed by the development of the new rosette. Almost certainly, there will be far too many seedlings germinating to grow them all, but after a few months the most promising ones can be transplanted and grown on.

One of the fascinations of growing sempervivums is that it is easy to raise and name new cultivars. This has, however, resulted in many cultivars being named that are very similar to each other. Before anyone decides to name a new variety they should have access to a very large collection of cultivars in order to be certain that the new plant is distinct enough to warrant a new name. There are well over 4000 named *Sempervivum* cultivars and more are added each year. Most of these have been raised by amateurs and many of those in cultivation have never been validly described.

The rules and regulations for the naming of new cultivars are set out in the **International Code of Nomenclature for Cultivated Plants**, Trehane, P., 1995

Pests and diseases

Sempervivums are well known for their ability to thrive under adverse conditions and to survive long periods of neglect or mistreatment. There are a few pests that will attack them and, although their effects are not often lethal, they can spoil the appearance of the plant and reduce its growth rate.

Vine weevils

The larvae of vine weevils (*Otiorhynchus sulcatus*) feed on the roots of sempervivums (and other plants) mainly during the autumn, winter and early spring. They seem to prefer the large, smooth leaved varieties to the hairy types and as the roots are eaten the rosette becomes detached from the soil and lies on the soil surface.

Vine weevil larvae

Remains of a rosette eaten by vine weevils

At this stage the larvae can often be found actually in the base of the plant but if not, they will be in the soil below. Provided that the actual growing point has not been eaten, the rosette can be rescued and if placed on fresh compost it will re-root.

Eventually the larvae can eat up through the stem of the rosette until all that remains are a few detached leaves and the plant will die.

If vine weevils are a problem the simplest treatment is to check each plant in the early spring and re-pot any that appear to be loose because have lost their roots. The larvae can then be found and destroyed.

A biological control method is available using a culture of parasitic nematode worms that attack and kill the vine weevil larvae. The treatment is expensive and best used for plants grown under glass. However, cultures are now available for outdoor use but they do require a certain minimum temperature to be effective.

If vine weevils are a severe problem they can be killed with insecticides. These are available to amateur gardeners under various trade names. Pre-treated compost is available or the insecticide can be bought as a chemical that can be watered onto infected pots.

Cutworms

Cutworms are the larvae of various night-flying moths. They feed on the roots in the same way as vine weevils and the effects on the plants are similar.

Cutworms are much larger than vine weevil larvae so they can do more damage. They are, however, easier to see and remove when a damaged plant is re-potted.

Cutworms

Root mealybugs

Plants infested with root mealybugs grow very slowly or may stop growing altogether if the infestation is heavy. Examination of the roots of an infested plant will reveal the presence of a bluish white, mould-like material (meal) that is secreted by the bugs as they feed. This substance may be most obvious on the inside of the pot. The insects themselves look something like tiny white woodlice but they are very small and hard to see.

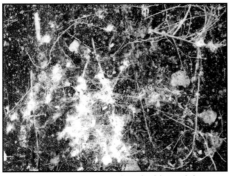
Appearance of roots infested with mealybug

Once they have been detected it is probably best to remove all infested roots from the plant, then re-pot it in fresh compost. The roots are usually unhealthy and come away from the plant quite easily as the old soil is removed. Washing with water may help to remove the mealybugs and their eggs. Pots that have held infested plants should be thoroughly cleaned before being used again.

It is rare for mealybug to be a severe problem and regular re-potting seems to keep the plants healthy enough to outgrow the pest.

Aphids

Occasionally, rosettes will be colonised by aphids (greenfly or blackfly) although this is rarely a serious problem. The aphids can usually be brushed off or, if necessary, plants can be sprayed with a suitable insecticide. Infected plants may be marked for a while but as new leaves grow they soon recover.

Diseases

It is rare to see houseleeks suffering from bacterial, virus or fungus infections. Under damp growing conditions the occasional rosette will rot away but this does not usually spread to other plants.

There is also a rust fungus, *Endophyllum sempervivi*, which can infect sempervivums. This causes some leaves to grow abnormally large then produces unsightly spots on the leaves but it is not usually a serious problem. It is best to destroy any unhealthy looking plants, and to make sure that the compost used is well drained. Normally no other treatment is necessary.

Sempervivum calcareum
The centre rosette of this group has rotted.

As a general rule, healthy plants will cope with, or out-grow the effects of most pests. It may be better to tolerate a small amount of damage or the occasional loss of a plant rather than immediately resort to chemical pesticides. Remedial treatment is usually only necessary when the balance between plants and their natural environment has been upset in some way and prevention is almost always better than cure.

19

Other problems
Birds
Birds can be a problem if they start digging up rosettes. Blackbirds in particular, will sometimes uproot newly planted rosettes although they appear less likely to go for established plants.

They do not feed on the rosettes and rarely actually carry them away but they search under them for food. Established plants that get attacked in this way are almost always found to be already damaged by vine weevils or other root feeding insects so the birds may, in fact, be preforming a useful service. The problem is that having found a few grubs, they may then get into the habit of searching all sempervivum pots.

Chickens can do a lot of damage if they get into an area where sempervivums are growing. They not only scrape at the soil, uprooting and scattering plants, but also they will peck at the more succulent types until the plant is completely destroyed.

Slugs and snails
Luckily, slugs and snails do not appear to be very keen on sempervivums. It may be that the leaves are too tough for them to eat, or perhaps there are other reasons why they avoid them, but it is rarely necessary to take any action against them. Just occasionally, they will graze on the cobweb types but then they mainly seem to eat the cobweb itself rather than the leaves.

Hail damage
A few days after a heavy hailstorm, sempervivums may develop spotting on their leaves. At first this looks as if they have been infected with a fungus disease but it is in fact, physical damage caused by the hailstones hitting the leaves. Each hit appears to damage a small patch of cells and this results in a pale coloured spot a few days later. The effect is most noticeable on the varieties that have dark coloured, wide spreading, glabrous leaves. The hairy types, and those with upright leaves, presumably do not suffer the damage because the hailstones are deflected.

There is no lasting damage to the plants but the rosettes will show the spots until new leaves have replaced the damaged ones.

Labels
Most people like to know the names of the plants that they are growing but it is difficult to find labels that last for more than a year or two outdoors. The ink from marker pens, even those designed for plant labels, tends to fade in the sunlight. Pencil writing and carbon based inks do not fade but they gradually get washed away by the rain. Engraved or embossed labels are relatively permanent but very expensive.

Label printing machines such as the **Brother P-touch** series print on adhesive-backed plastic tape in a wide range of colours. The printed tapes can be stuck onto plastic or metal labels and will last for many years. The printers and tapes are quite expensive, but if a large number of labels is needed they are much more economical than engraved labels. There is also the advantage that labels can be automatically generated from a computer database.

Whatever labels are used, there is always a chance that the label will be accidently lost, or pulled out by birds. If it is important to make sure that a plant is always identifiable then it is always worth having a second label buried in the pot or the soil near the plants. Pencil writing on a plastic label will last for many years underground.

Sempervivum species

Introduction

The genus *Sempervivum* is generally considered to contain about 50 species but the nomenclature is still open to debate. There are a large number of species described in the literature and an even greater number of names applied to plants in cultivation.

Most species show a wide range of variation especially under different cultivation conditions and many will freely hybridize. In the past it has been very easy to consider a collected clone to be sufficiently different from others to warrant a separate name. Consequently, many of those that have been named as species are probably just varieties of one species, hybrids between species, or even just a variant individual clone.

Sempervivum arachnoideum

It is also very difficult to identify an individual plant when it is out of its natural habitat, especially when only the vegetative rosettes are available.

Many plants in collections are incorrectly named and of dubious origin. For the enthusiast, this makes the group interesting but it can be frustrating for the botanist who wants to build up an accurately named collection. The most desirable specimens are those that are correctly identified and from a named location with field data.

Gérard Dumont, has made an extensive study of the genus *Sempervivum* and related species. On the basis of detailed investigations of the structure, distribution, ecology, physiology and genetics of the plants he has proposed a classification system for the genus that builds on, and refines the historical nomenclature. Full details of this work are described on his website at: http://sempervivophilia.free.fr/

The list of species in the following section is based on Gérard Dumont's 'Nomenclatural Explorer' as published on his website. The species are divided into two main groups on the basis of their flower colour; those with predominantly red flowers (**Section Rhodanthae**), and those with yellow flowers (**Section Chrysanthae**). Within each of these groups the species are listed alphabetically. This arrangement is artificial and does not reflect the biological relationships but is a convenient way of arranging plants in a collection.

The name of each species is followed by the naming authority, the country or place of origin and, where possible, a brief description or a photograph of the plant in cultivation. Where species names that are in common use have been demoted to subspecies or varieties the previously accepted name is given in brackets.

Gérard Dumont has proposed that the genus *Jovibarba* is included as a subgenus of *Sempervivum.* This may well be justified, but many people are familiar with using the name *Jovibarba* so we have continued to use it in this publication.

Section Rhodanthae
Red flowered species

S. altum Turrill (1936) - Caucasus Mts
- var. ***altum*** - Medium size, pale green
succulent leaves with reddish tips.

Sempervivum altum var. *altum*

Sempervivum altum var. *altum* - flowers

Offsets are produced on long stolons.
- var. ***ossetiense*** - (***S. ossetiense*** Wale) -
Similar to var. ***altum*** but leaves are
shorter and more succulent; pale green

Sempervivum altum var. *ossetiense*

with small dark tips. Flat, open rosettes.

S. annae Gurgenidze (1969) - Caucasus
Mts - There is some doubt as to whether
the clones in cultivation with this name are
correctly identified.

S. arachnoideum L. (1753) - European
Mts - **The Cobweb Houseleek**. The leaf
tips are connected by a white cobweb of
hairs. There are many varieties that differ
in colour, size and degree of cobweb.
<u>Photos: Page 4, 16 and 21</u>

- var. ***bryoides*** -
Very small moss-
like rosettes. It is
probably better to
consider this as a
small growing form
of *S. arachnoideum*
rather than a true
botanical variety.

S. arachnoideum
var. *bryoides*

- var. ***tomentosum*** -
Similar to the type
plant but typically
has larger rosettes
with a more dense
cobweb. Some
clones develop
reddish outer leaves
in the summer.

S. arachnoideum
var. *tomentosum*

S. arachnoideum '**Album**' - An
interesting variety that has pure white
flowers. The rosette leaves are pale
green. It is rather slow-growing and has
a tendency to flower frequently so is
rather difficult to keep. <u>Photo: Page 7</u>

S. arachnoideum
'**Cristate**' - This
form, which has
abnormal congested
growth, is rather
slow growing and
tends to revert back
to normal rosettes.

S. arachnoideum
'Cristate'

S. arachnoideum '**Hookeri**' - Very small, narrow leaved rosettes that soon grow into dense, moss-like cushions. (Also seen named as ×*barbulatum* 'Hookeri')

Sempervivum arachnoideum 'Hookeri'

S. atlanticum Ball (1878) - Morocco - Medium size, rather open rosettes that soon grow into a dense group. Bright green leaves all

S. atlanticum

through the year. This is the only *Sempervivum* species native to Africa.

Sempervivum atlanticum from Oukaimeden

S. atlanticum '**Edward Balls**' - The rosettes of this cultivar are more globular in shape and they flush with brownish red in the summer. The clone was probably collected in the wild.

S. calcareum Jordan (1849) - French SW Alps - Medium to large, grey-green or bluish green rosettes. The leaves of most forms have dark reddish-brown tips.

There are a large number of different regional varieties and cultivars of this species, many of which make very attractive garden plants.

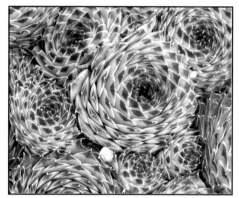

Sempervivum calcareum from Alps France

S. calcareum
from Céüse

S. calcareum
from Guillaumes

In cultivation, plants of *S. calcareum* are rather slow to flower, which means that large impressive clumps soon build up. The flowers are pale in colour and petals shade from cream to pinkish-red at the base.

S. calcareum
from Mt Ventoux

S. calcareum
from Céüse

23

Some examples of *S. calcareum* cultivars.

'Extra'

'Limelight'

'Sir William Lawrence'

'Monstrosum'

'Tip Top'

S. cantabricum Huber (1934) - North and Central Spain - Deep green pubescent leaves often with dark brown tips. A very attractive species with many geographical forms. Some types tend to lose many of their outer leaves in the winter but they usually recover in the spring.
- subsp. *cantabricum* - Northern Spain - Clones in cultivation include those collected from Lago de Enol, Lietariegos, Piedrafita, Riaño, Puerto de San Glorio, Puerto de Somiedo and Vegarada.
- subsp. *guadarramense* - M.C. Smith (1981) - Central Spain - Clones from Pico del Lobo and Navafria.

S. cantabricum subsp. *guadarramense* from Navafria

- subsp. *urbionense* - M.C. Smith (1981) - Spain - Medium sized globular rosettes, offsets on short thick stolons. (Sometimes named as **S. vicentei**.) Clones from Picos de Urbion, Valvanera and El Gaton are in cultivation.

S. caucasicum Rupr. (1969) - Caucasus Mts - Small to medium size open rosettes. Leaves develop a dark red-brown colour in the spring but remain attractive throughout the year.

Sempervivum caucasicum

- var. *borissovae* (**S. borissovae** Wale) - Caucasus Mts - Small rosettes, bright green leaves with dark brown tips and silver cilia. An attractive species producing large numbers of offsets but sensitive to winter damp.

S. caucasicum var. *borissovae*

S. charadzeae Gurgenidze (1969) - Caucasus Mts - Very large open rosettes of wide yellowish green leaves with tiny dark tips. Pale pink flowers. The offsets are produced on very long stolons. See Photo: Page 6

Sempervivum charadzeae

S. dolomiticum Facchini (1855) - South-Eastern Alps - Small size, dark green rosettes with narrow pointed upright leaves.

S. dominii Konop & Konopova (1984) - Caucasus Mts.

S. dzhavachischvilii Gurgenidze (1969) - Caucasus Mts - Small greyish green, succulent, upright leaves with a neat dark tip. Tends to grow in tight clusters of rosettes. Rather sensitive to winter damp.

Sempervivum dzhavachisckvilii

S. ermanicum Gurgenidze (1969) - Caucasus Mts.

S. gurgenidzeae Priszter (1991) - Caucasus Mts.

S. ingwersenii Wale (1942) - Caucasus Mts - Small to medium size, open rosettes with few succulent dull green leaves, long stolons.

S. iranicum Born. & Gauba (1940) - Northern Iran.

S. kosaninii Praeger (1930) - Yugoslavia - Medium size, dark green velvety leaves. Produces many offsets on long stolons.

S. macedonicum Praeger (1930) - Yugoslavia - Small rosettes with narrow, tapering leaves, dull green flushed with pink.

S. macedonicum

S. marmoreum Griseb. (1843) - Balkans - A very variable species with a number of subspecies, several of which were originally described as individual species.

- subsp. **marmoreum** var. **marmoreum** - Balkans
- subsp. **marmoreum** var. **dinaricum** - a form from the Dinaric Alps.
- subsp. **ballsii** (**S. ballsii**) - The Type plant was collected by Edward Balls in 1937 from Mt Tschumba Petzi.

S. marmoreum subsp. *ballsii*
from Mt. Tschumba Petzi

25

- subsp. *matricum* (*S. matricum* Letz) - Slovakia. The rosette leaves are covered with a fine pubescence. It is said to grow to a large size but is difficult to keep through the winter.

S. marmoreum subsp. *matricum*

- subsp. *reginae-amaliae* (*S. reginae-amaliae* Heldr.) - Greece and Albania - Medium sized, dense leaved, open rosettes. There are several different geographical clones in cultivation.

S. marmoreum subsp. *reginae-amaliae* from Mavri Petri

subsp. *reginae-amaliae* var. *erythraeum* (*S. erythraeum* Velenovsky) - Bulgaria - A beautiful form with velvety grey-green leaves often tinged pink. Requires protection in the winter Photo: Page 5

S. marmoreum '**Brunneifolium**' - An attractive cultivar with pinkish brown leaves and short thick stolons.

S. marmoreum 'Brunneifolium'

S. montanum L. (1753) - **The Mountain Houseleek**. Widely distributed through the European Mts, usually at high altitude. Small growing, early flowering plants often with a distinct resinous odour. There are four subspecies and a number of varieties.

- subsp. *montanum* - SW Alps, Corsica - Small rosettes often with a frosted appearance.

- subsp. *carpaticum* - Western Carpathians -Pale green, more open rosettes.

S. montanum subsp. *montanum*   *S. montanum* subsp. *carpaticum*

- subsp. *carpaticum* '**Cmiral's Yellow**' - A cultivar whose leaves are bright yellow in the spring and early summer. A striking plant but rather difficult to grow. Photo: Page 4

- subsp. *heterophyllum* - Western Carpathians - Large and open rosettes.

- subsp. *stiriacum* - Eastern Alps - Longer narrower leaves usually with dark tips.

S. montanum subsp. *stiriacum*

S. montanum subsp. *stiriacum*

S. nevadense Wale (1941) - Southern Spain - Medium size clustering rosettes with short, glabrous or hairy, reddish-brown tipped leaves. The rosettes become flushed with pinkish-brown in the summer. The amount of pubescence varies in different clones.

Sempervivum nevadense

S. pumilum Bieb. (1808) - Caucasus Mts - Small globular rosettes with keeled, pointed leaves and silver cilia. Flowers are a pretty rose-pink colour. The species is quite variable and a number of distinctly different clones are in cultivation.

Sempervivum pumilum

The form No.1 from Adyl Su has many small rosettes of bright yellowish-green leaves and rapidly grows into an attractive cluster of rosettes.

Sempervivum pumilum from Adyl Su, No.1

S. tectorum L. (1753) - European Mts - This is **The Common Houseleek** seen in many gardens and often found growing on walls and old roof-tops. A number of subspecies and geographical varieties are recognised but there are many intermediate forms.

- subsp. ***tectorum*** - generally large growing plants but there are a number of distinct varieties.

Sempervivum tectorum subsp. *tectorum*

- subsp. ***arvernense*** - average size rosettes often with velvety leaves.

- subsp. ***boutignyanum*** - Pyrenees - A small, compact form with rather succulent leaves.

Sempervivum tectorum subsp. *boutignyanum*

- subsp. ***decoloratum*** - large pale leaved plants often shaded with pinkish-purple.

- subsp. ***italicum*** - velvety leaves, plants often with long stolons.

(*S. tectorum* var. *alpinum*) - A name commonly used in horticulture for small growing forms of *S. tectorum*.

Section Chrysanthae
Yellow flowered species

S. armenum Boiss. & Huet. (1856) - Turkey - Medium size, dull green leaves with dark tips.
- subsp. **armenum** - Similar in appearance to *S. tectorum* but with yellowish-green flowers.
- subsp. **sosnowskyi** - (**S. sosnowskyi** Ter-Chatsch) - Medium sized rosettes of wide, succulent leaves, pale green with dark tips.

S. ciliosum Craib. (1914) - Bulgaria, Macedonica, Albania - A very attractive species. Small, many-leaved, symmetrical rosettes. Leaves with long marginal cilia. Rather sensitive to damp so it is best to keep plants under cover through the winter. <u>Photo: Page 5</u>
- subsp. **ciliosum** - yellow petals without a basal spot. There are two varieties:
- var. **ciliosum** - the normal green form.

S. ciliosum

S. ciliosum subsp. *ciliosum* var. *ciliosum*

- var. **galicicum** - globose rosettes that take on a deep red colour in the summer. A beautiful variety that looks almost like a small cactus.

var. *galicicum*

- subsp. **octopodes** - (**S. octopodes** Turrill) - distinguished from subsp. *ciliosum* by the presence of a red spot at the base of the petals. It also has longer stolons.

The clone most commonly seen in cultivation is a form known as *octopodes* var. *apetalum*. This clone, whose flowers lack petals, is slightly larger, produces numerous offsets on very long stolons and is easy to grow. It is an individual monstrose variation rather than a true botanical variety.

S. ciliosum subsp. *octopodes*   Flowers of var. *apetalum*

The rosettes occasionally develop into spectacular monstrose forms.

S.ciliosum subsp. *octopodes* - monstrose rosettes

S. grandiflorum Haworth (1821) - NW Italy - Large dull green leaves that are covered with small glandular hairs which makes them feel almost sticky to the touch. Strong resinous odour and large attractive yellow flowers.

S. grandiflorum

28

S. ispartae Muirhead (1969) - Turkey - Small, open rosettes of glabrous leaves.

S. minus Turrill (1940) - Turkey - Small olive green rosettes, flushed with red in the summer. Needs winter protection.

S. pittonii Schott (1854) - Austria - A very attractive species with small hairy leaves. Each leaf has a brown apical spot. It produces a large number of offsets which cluster around the main plant but it is rather sensitive to winter damp. Although fairly common in cultivation, it is restricted to two small areas of serpentine rock in the wild.

S. ruthenicum subsp. *zeleborii* var. *zeleborii*

Sempervivum pittonii

Detail of the flowers of the above plant showing the basal red spots on the petals.

var. zeleborii

S. ruthenicum (1855) Schnittsp. - Carpates, Ukraine and Balkans - Medium to large rosettes of upright, pale green pubescent leaves. The species can be divided into two subspecies and a number of related forms, some of which were originally described as separate species.

- subsp. *ruthenicum* - Carpates and Ukraine - larger rosettes, petals without a basal red spot.
- subsp. *zeleborii* - Balkans - smaller growing, petals with a distinct red basal spot. Three forms in cultivation, that are commonly labelled as species, are probably best considered as varieties of subsp. *zeleborii*.

- var. *zeleborii* (*S. zelebori*)
- var. *kindingeri* (*S. kindingeri*)
- var. *leucanthum* (*S. leucanthum*)

S. ruthenicum subsp. *zeleborii* var. *kindingeri*

All of the plants in the *S. ruthenicum* group are sensitive to winter damp and do best if they are protected from rain in the winter.

S. staintonii Muirhead (1969) - Turkey - Small succulent rosettes. Leaves glabrous.

S. transcaucasicum Muirhead (1965) - This is another large group of related plants, many of which have been described as species but are probably better considered as subspecies or varieties.
- subsp. **transcaucasicum**
- subsp. **gillianii**
  - var. **gillianii** (*S. gillanii*)
  - var. **brevipilum** (*S. brevipilum*)
  - var. **pisidicum** (*S. pisidicum*)
- subsp. **davisii** (*S. davisii*)

Many of the plants in cultivation under the names *S. brevipilum*, *S. davisii*, and *S. transcaucasicum* are of dubious origin. They are however attractive plants to grow although most require winter protection.

Plants in cultivation as
S. transcaucasicum (Left) and *S. davisii* (Right)

S. wulfenii Hoppe (1831) - Two subspecies are recognised:
- subsp. **wulfenii** - Austrian and Swiss Alps - Medium to large pale green, glabrous rosettes with wide, upright, pointed leaves. It produces few offsets so is slow to propagate.
- subsp. **juvanii** (Strgar) Fav. & Parn. - Slovenia - distinguished by having pubescent leaves and by its geographical location.

Sempervivum wulfenii subsp. *wulfenii*

In cultivation, *S. wulfenii* is rather slow at producing offsets. Occasionally a rosette will produce several offsets but more commonly there are only one or two.

S. wulfenii subsp. wulfenii

Interspecific hybrids

Sempervivum species interbreed relatively easily and produce offspring that often show characteristics that are intermediate between the parents. Some of the better known hybrids have been given names while others are just known by the names of the probable parent species.

Under natural conditions the distribution of different species often overlaps, and hybridisation can then occur. Frequently the hybrids themselves can produce fertile seeds but even if they are sterile they can reproduce by means of offsets. These hybrids have sometimes been collected and described as new species. A number of clones in cultivation fall into this category.

Many other crosses have been made artificially and propagated as garden plants. The following page describes just a few of the hybrids that are in cultivation.

S. ×*christii* Wolf (*S. grandiflorum* × *S. montanum*) - Deep green, pubescent leaves with dark tips, pinkish yellow flowers.

S. ×*funckii* Braun (? *S. arachnoideum* × *S. montanum* × *S. tectorum*) - Bright green, tightly packed leaves. Red flowers. This plant is well known in cultivation but its true botanical status is not certain.

S. (×)*giuseppii* Wale - (? *S. cantabricum* × *S. arachnoideum*). Originally described as a species from Northern Spain but now thought to be a hybrid. There are a number of clones in cultivation and most are quite prolific.

Sempervivum (×)*giuseppii*

S. ×*thompsonianum* Wale (1940) - Yugoslavia - Small, neat, many-leaved rosettes, producing offsets on long stolons. Buff coloured flowers. Possibly a natural hybrid between *S. macedonicum* and (*S. ciliosum*).

Sempervivum ×*thompsonianum*

S. ×*vaccarii* Vaccari (*S. arachnoideum* × *S. grandiflorum*) - NW Italy - Medium size, open rosettes, slightly hairy. Pinkish flowers.

S. ×*widderi* Lehm. & Schnittsp (*S. tectorum* × *S. wulfenii*) - Central and Eastern Alps - Medium sized, dull green rosettes. Rare in the wild.

The cultivated forms of the following hybrids are probably all of garden origin.

S. *arachnoideum* × *calcareum* - Very attractive, large rosettes of pale green, hairy leaves with red tips. Pink flowers.

S. arachnoideum × *calcareum*

S. *arachnoideum* × *nevadense* - Green leaves flushed with orange-red, tufts of hairs at leaf tips.

S. *arachnoideum* × *pittonii* - Globular, clustering, hairy rosettes, greyish green.

S. *ciliosum* × *marmoreum* - Attractive, hairy rosettes which are intermediate between the parents.

S. *grandiflorum* × *ciliosum* - Similar to *S. grandiflorum* but smaller and with hairier leaves.

S. *pumilum* × *ingwersenii* - medium size rosettes which produce large numbers of offsets. In the summer the rosettes are a dark red colour.

Sempervivum cultivars

Introduction

The term **cultivar** is used to describe a group of cultivated plants that can be clearly distinguished from others and which retain their distinguishing characteristics when reproduced. Over the hundreds of years that houseleeks have been cultivated many new forms have arisen as a result of interbreeding or mutations. Many of these have been given cultivar names and then propagated vegetatively by means of offsets.

In 1982 the **Sempervivum Society,** which at that time acted as the International Registration Authority for cultivars, published the **International Register of *Sempervivum* and *Jovibarba* Cultivars** containing about a thousand varieties. Since then, many others have been produced, mainly by amateur enthusiasts, and there are now over four thousand named cultivars. Many of these names are in common use but have not been validly published.

The Sempervivum Society is no longer in operation but a comprehensive list of *Sempervivum* and *Jovibarba* cultivars has been produced by Martin Miklánek and can be found on his website at: http://members.tripod.com/~miklanek/ The latest version of this list is also available on Gérard Dumont's website at: http://sempervivophilia.free.fr/

With over 4000 different named *Sempervivum* cultivars it is impossible to show anything but a tiny selection here. The photographs on the following pages are of various plants from our **NCCPG National Collection®**. They are arranged alphabetically, and selected to illustrate the range of different forms that are available.

The cultivar name is followed by the country of origin, (AT = Austria; BE = Belgium; CH = Switzerland; CZ = Czech Republic; DE = Germany; FR = France; NL = The Netherlands; UK = Great Britain; US = United States of America), a very brief description and a photograph.

The appearance of any individual plant varies greatly with its age, the growing conditions and the time of the year. Photographs only show a particular plant at a certain moment in time and the same cultivar my appear quite different at another time, or when growing in a different environment.

Sempervivum 'Red Spider'
Photographed in late August

Sempervivum 'Red Spider'
The same plant the follwing April

It is almost impossible to identify an unknown cultivar from photographs or descriptions, or even by direct comparison with other growing plants. Also, many plants sold by garden centres are seed raised, and although they may be beautiful plants it would be incorrect to identify them as named cultivars.

If a few previously identified plants have had their labels mixed up, or if the name is only partially readable, then by comparison with other named plants it is possible to reunite the plants with their labels. Without at least some clue to its name, an unidentified cultivar will probably have to remain so.

A selection of Sempervivum cultivars

'Aalrika' - BE - Beautiful large rosettes of deep red leaves with silver edges. Impressive all year round but rather slow to propagate.

'Aalrika'

'Adelmoed' - BE - Wide rosettes of pinkish grey, glaucous leaves.

'Adelmoed'

'Aladdin' - BE - A fast-growing *S. arachnoideum* type cultivar.

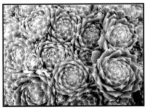

'Aladdin'

'Alchimist' - BE - Unusual yellowish-brown leaves and nicely shaped rosettes. Rather similar to 'Bernstein' but the leaf

tips are not as strongly marked.

'Alchimist'

'Agnes' - BE - Large hairy rosettes, pale green but flushed with pinkish-brown in the summer

'Agnes'

'Amanda' - UK - A fast growing cultivar with dark purple-brown, long tapering leaves.

'Amanda'

'Aross' - NL - The long narrow leaves go dark glossy red in the summer. Each leaf has a distinct tuft of white apical hairs.

'Aross'

'Atropurpureum' - ? - A cultivar of *S. tectorum*. The leaves are a dark blackish-purple in the spring and remain a good colour all through the year.

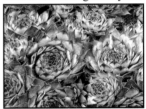

'Atropurpureum'

'Bedivere' - US - Bright red, smooth, abruptly pointed leaves, a small neat grower.

'Bedivere'

'Bernstein' - DE - Large attractive rosettes, greenish gold with shades of pink and red. The best colours develop in the flowering rosettes as the leaves elongate and become edged with red.

'Bernstein'

'Bethany' - DE - Attractive rosettes of silvery green leaves covered with tiny hairs. The leaf bases become flused with pink in the summer.

'Bethany'

'Black Mountain' - NL - An attractive and vigorous cultivar. Dark blackish-red leaves covered with fine pubescence.

'Black Mountain'

'Blue Boy' - US - Greyish-green rosettes that take on a very attractive blue tinge in the summer. Sturdy, compact plants that offset well.

'Blue Boy'

'Boissieri' - UK - An attractive bronze-green cultivar of *S. tectorum*. One of the earliest named cultivars. Photo: Page 3

'Bronco' - DE - Dark, sharply pointed leaves that are a glossy brownish-red in the summer. Good colours all the year round and quite a fast grower.

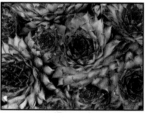
'Bronco'

'Bronze Pastel' - UK - Small, clustering rosettes with incurved leaves. An unusual and attractive bronze colour shading to orange in the autumn. Relatively large, bright pink flowers.

'Bronze Pastel'

'Butterbur' - US - Large flat rosettes of many small leaves. Photo: Page 8

'Cherry Tart' - UK - Beautiful symmetrical rosettes of glossy purplish-black leaves. Very few offsets are produced so this cultivar is likely to remain rare in cultivation.

'Cherry Tart'

'Corsair' - UK - Large, vigorously growing rosettes producing many offsets. Leaves change from green to dark red and have long silvery hairs.

'Corsair'

'Crispyn' - BE - Dark greyish-purple rosettes of pointed leaves.

'Crispyn'

34

'Dagdad Cafe' - BE - Small dark leaved rosettes with dense white cobweb.

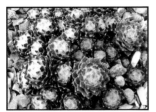
'Dagdad Cafe'

'Dark Cloud' - US - Large, many-leaved symmetrical rosettes, dark purple with greyish shadows.

'Dark Cloud'

'Deep Fire' - US - Greyish green leaves with long silvery marginal hairs, shading to wine red in the centre. In the spring the whole plant turns glowing red.

'Deep Fire'

'Dorisa' - BE - Dark red leaves edged with silver hairs.

'Dorisa'

'Downland Queen' - UK - Pale greyish green leaves shading to khaki.

'Downland Queen'

'Dyke' - UK - Rosettes of intense dark red, glossy leaves. Green in winter.

'Dyke'

'Emerald Giant' - US - Large rosettes of emerald green leaves. The flowers have cream petals with a greenish central stripe.

'Emerald Giant'

'Emmchen' - BE - Tight, compact rosettes of bright green leaves with neat dark tips.

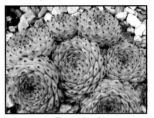
'Emmchen'

'Engle's 13-2' - US - Short, succulent leaves, greyish purple and covered with fine down. Rather slow growing.

'Engle's 13-2'

'Exorna' - UK - Beautiful velvety leaves in shades of olive green and pink. Takes on a bronzed appearance in the summer. Unusual pinkish brown flowers.

'Exorna'

'Fire Glint' - UK - Medium sized rosettes, shades of green and brown but glowing brownish red in the spring and summer.

'Fire Glint'

'Fronika' - BE - Dense rosettes of narrow leaves in various shades of green and red and covered with fine down. The rosettes turn brownish-red in the spring.

'Fronika'

'Fuego' - DE - Large rosettes of deep purplish-red leaves. Very good winter colour.

'Fuego'

'Gallivarda' - BE - Large, bright red, wide open rosettes. Excellent colour all through the year.
Photos: Page 4

'Georgette' - UK - Small clustering rosettes. Shades of green, pink and red in the summer.

'Georgette'

'Granby' - UK - Medium size, open rosettes which are very bright red through most of the year.

'Granby'

'Graupurpur' - DE - Large rosettes of wide, deep purplish-red leaves.
Photo: Page 4

'Green Disk' - UK - small flattened rosettes of olive green leaves with small dark apical spot.

'Green Disk'

'Grey Velvet' - US - Lovely grey-green rosettes with fine pubescence.

'Grey Velvet'

'Gulle Dame' - BE - Dark red leaves edged with long silver hairs. The rosettes soon develop into a large clump. Very colourful through the spring and summer but the leaves are green in the winter.

'Gulle Dame'

'Hart' - DE - In winter the leaves are short and green, becoming longer and turning a glowing orange-red in the spring and summer.

'Hart'

'Hayling' - UK - Large, open rosettes of glossy leaves that are a very dark purplish-red. In the spring they can be almost black.

'Hayling'

'Hester' - US - Medium sized, open rosettes. Red and green, velvety leaves, edged with white hairs

'Hester'

'Hopi' - DE - Brownish-orange rosettes that turn red-brown in the spring.

'Hopi'

'Irazu' - DE - Reddish violet leaves shading to green at the tips.

'Irazu'

'Jet Stream' - US - Small, symmetrical rosettes, dark purplish red with silver cilia. Small flowers of pale cream petals with pinkish red tips.

'Jet Stream'

'Jewel Case' - US - Small, dense clustering rosettes. Bright pinkish red leaves outlined with silver hairs. Photo: Page 16

'Jungle Fires' - US - Large purplish-red rosettes. Very good spring and summer colour.

'Jungle Fires'

'Justine's Choice' - ? - Leaves range from grey to pinkish-olive green. The rosettes usually produce many offsets.

'Justine's Choice'

'Koko Flanel' - BE - Greyish green, many-leaved and very symmetrical rosettes, covered with white hair.

'Koko Flanel'

'Korspelsegietje' - BE - Very variable through the year. Glowing red in the spring, darker brown in the summer, fading to green and brown in the autumn.

'Korspelsegietje' (May)

'Korspelsegietje' (September)

'Kramer's Spinrad' - BE - One of the largest *S. arachnoideum* cultivars. Densely cobwebbed in the summer. The green leaves flush with red in the spring. Very impressive flowers. Photo: Page 7

37

'Kramer's Spinrad'

'Lavender and Old Lace'
- UK - Medium size, with
leaves of a beautiful
lavender colour, edged
with silver cilia.

'Lavender and Old Lace'

'Lilac Time' - UK - Large
rosettes with elegant
shaped leaves. A beautiful
pale lilac colour in the
summer, shading to pink at
the tips.

'Lilac Time'

'Lively Bug' - US - Very
hairy rosettes, medium
size, greyish green but
flushed with purplish-red
in the summer. A vigorous
grower that usually
produces a lot of offsets.

'Lively Bug'

'Leon Smits' - BE - Bright
red, elongated leaves in the
spring and summer.

'Leon Smits'

'Lynn's Choice' - US -
Large velvety leaves that
are an unusual brownish-
green colour with pink
overtones..

'Lynn's Choice'

'Mahogany' - UK - A
beautiful dark reddish-
brown most of the year.

'Mahogany'

'Melanie' - DE - Large
downy rosettes, bluish-
green with dark brown
tips.

'Melanie'

'Midas' - UK - Neat
rosettes of narrow green
leaves, tipped with red in
the summer. A cultivar of
S. montanum.

'Midas'

'Moerkerk's Merit' - BE
- Greyish green, densely
hairy. The outer leaves are
flushed with brownish-
purple in the summer.

'Moerkerk's Merit'

'Mondstein' - DE - Large
olive green rosettes that
are flushed with red. The
offsets are globular and
tend to rise up over the
parent rosettes.

'Mondstein'

'Mulberry Wine' - US - Long pointed leaves, shading from a rich purple-red to green at the tips. Lovely colours in the spring and summer.

'Mulberry Wine'

'Neon' - DE - The leaves of this cultivar are an unusual greenish-gold colour with dark brown tips. The rosettes are dense and compact.

'Neon'

'Oddity' - US - A cultivar of *S. tectorum* that has leaves that are curved backwards on themselves so that they become almost tubular at the tips.

'Oddity'

'Olga' - BE - Medium sized rosettes of intense greyish-purple turning much darker through the summer.

'Olga'

'Passionata' - BE - The leaves are olive green but with beautiful, and difficult to describe, overtones of gold, pink and red in the spring.

'Passionata'

'Pastel' - UK - Small to medium size, unusual pinkish-bronze leaves.

'Pastel'

'Packardian' - US - Very large rosettes of velvety red leaves.

'Packardian'

'Petsy' - UK - Lovely fresh yellow-green leaves that are bright all the year round. It is probably just a clone of *S. atlanticum.*

'Petsy'

'Pippin' - US - Medium size, symmetrical, many-leaved rosettes, dark brownish red.

'Pippin'

'Purdy's 50-6' - US - Green leaves flushed with dark brown, especially on the edges. Sharply pointed leaf tips. The flowers have pale cream petals with green centre stripe.

'Purdy's 50-6'

'Pygmalion' - UK - Small, clustering rosettes with dense white cobweb in the summer. *S. arachnoideum* cultivar.

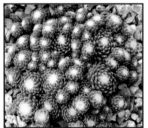
'Pygmalion'

'Quintessence' - US - Large shapely rosettes of wide leaves that are various shades of dark purple. They can go almost black at times.

'Quintessence'

'Red Ace' - UK - Long, narrow, rather soft, pointed leaves with silver marginal hairs. The leaves are green in the winter but in the spring and summer they turn bright carmine red.

'Red Ace'

'Red Lion' - BE - Bright red rosettes with silver cilia. Small growing but produces a lot of offsets.

'Red Lion'

'Red Lynn' - BE - The rosettes are a wonderful blackish-purple in the spring. This changes to rich red later.

'Red Lynn'

'Reggy' - BE - Very large, symmetrical rosettes of brownish-red leaves.

'Reggy'

'Reinhardt' - DE - Tight rosettes of emerald green, upright leaves with sharply contrasting black tips. A beautiful variety that grows well and looks good all the year round.

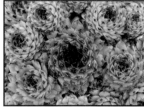
'Reinhardt'

'Rita Jane' - US - Large, greyish green rosettes, flushed with pink. Small dark tips on the leaves.

'Rita Jane'

'Rotkopf' - DE - Shapely leaves, pinkish brown and pubescent. A beautiful cultivar, especially in late summer when the leaf tips turn orange.

'Rotkopf'

'Sharon's Pencil' - US - Large rosettes of greenish-gold leaves that have long brown points. Tends to flower rather freely.

'Sharon's Pencil'

'Silver Thaw' - US - Small greyish-green rosettes with a dense covering of silver hairs. Photo: Page 4

'Silverine' - US - Large pale silver-grey rosettes. Rather slow to produce offsets.

'Silverine'

'Skrocki's Beauty' - BE - Densly clustering hairy rosettes that flush with red in the summer.

'Skrocki's Beauty'

'Slabber's Seedling' - ? - Unusual dark greyish pink rosettes. Offsets on thick stolons. Large flowers with narrow brownish pink petals.

'Slabber's Seedling'

'Starburst' - UK - Large rosettes of dark purple leaves tipped and outlined with greyish-green. Photos: Page 6

'Starburst'

'Sun Waves'- US - Open rosettes of short, wide, glossy leaves that are a very unusual shade of pinkish-gold.

'Sun Waves'

'Sunset' - DE - A lovely form of *S. tectorum*.

'Sunset'

'Tarita' - BE - Large, dark purplish-red rosettes with grey overtones.

'Tarita'

'Thunder' - US - Shapely rosettes that are pale olive green heavily flushed with pink, especially in winter.

'Thunder'

'Tordeur's Memory' - BE - The rosettes are dull green in the winter but from the spring through to summer they are intense, shining red. Long narrow leaves with silver cilia.

'Tordeur's Memory'

'Twilight Blues' - US - Medium size, attractively shaped rosettes. The leaves take on a lovely violet-blue shade in the summer. Photo: Page 4

'Tristesse' - BE - A lovely compact form. The leaves are unusual shades of olive green, brown and purple.

'Tristesse'

'Van Baelen' - BE - Large, attractively shaped rosettes. Pinkish-purple leaves shading to green. Leaf tips abruptly narrow to a long sharp point.

'Van Baelen'

'Virgil' - US - Medium size rosettes. The leaves are various shades of purple, violet and grey.

'Virgil'

'Virginius' - US - Bright green, rather soft rosettes. Leaves with a reddish-brown tip. Produces many offsets on short stolons so groups up well. Cream flowers.

'Virginius'

'Waterlily' - BE - Dark purple and green rosettes that are attractively shaped but slow to offset. <u>Photo: Page 16</u>

'White Christmas' - BE - Small pale green rosettes with a dense, pure white cobweb in the summer.

'White Christmas'

'Woolcott's Variety' - US - The leaves shade from greyish-pink at the base to greenish-gold at the tips.

'Woolcott's Variety'

'Zenith' - US - Small, bright green rosettes that produce large numbers of offsets. Possibly a clone of *S. cantabricum*. <u>Photo: Page 16</u>

'Zepherin' - BE - Dark blackish-purple rosettes that have very good winter colour.

'Zepherin'

'Zilver Moon' - BE - Small, light green rosettes with white hairs. The outer leaves shade to pinkish-red in the summer. Pale pink flowers.

'Zilver Moon'

'Zilver Susanna' - BE - A *S. arachnoideum* cultivar that has dark red leaves in the spring and summer that contrast well with the white cobweb.

'Zilver Suzanna'

Jovibarba

Introduction

Originally, the plants known as jovibarbas (**Jove's Beard**) were included within the genus *Sempervivum* but they were later placed in a genus of their own, primarily on the basis of their different flower structure.

A number of species of *Jovibarba* have been described and five names are still in common use: *J. allionii, J. arenaria, J. hirta, J. sobolifera* and *J. heuffelii*. The first four of these are very similar and are probably better considered as subspecies rather than species. They all produce offsets on short, fragile stolons. The offsets, which are sometimes known as **rollers**, are almost spherical and easily become detached, and roll away from the parent plant.

The fifth species, *Jovibarba heuffelii* is different in that it reproduces vegetatively by splitting of the main stem into two or more rosettes rather than by the production of offsets on stolons.

Gérard Dumont has suggested that the jovibarbas should be considered as a subgenus of *Sempervivum*. In this case, the name *Sempervivum globiferum* would be used to include the plants known as *J. allionii, J. arenaria, J. hirta,* and *J. sobolifera,* and *Sempervivum heuffelii* would be used in place of *Jovibarba heuffelii.*

Because of the differences in flower structure between *Sempervivum* and *Jovibarba* (<u>See Page 1</u>) we prefer to continue using the name *Jovibarba* as a genus. In the following list we have used the old species names but grouped them according to Gérard Dumont's classification and given his proposed names in brackets.

Jovibarba species

J. allionii (*Sempervivum globiferum* subsp. *allionii*) - SW Alps - Rosettes are a pale yellowish green and have long tapering incurved leaves that are covered with short glandular hairs.

J. arenaria (*Sempervivum globiferum* subsp. *arenarium*) - Austria and Italy - Very small, globular rosettes, green, orange and dark red. It grows best in a very well drained soil and benefits from some protection from winter damp.

J. arenaria

J. hirta subsp. ***hirta*** (*Sempervivum globiferum* subsp. *hirtum*) - Eastern Alps and W. Carpathians - Small rosettes of glabrous leaves, in shades of green, red and brown. Very variable in form.

J. hirta subsp. ***glabrescens*** (*Sempervivum globiferum* subsp. *glabrescens*) - W. Carpathians - Incurved leaves, heavily flushed with dark red.

J. hirta subsp. ***tatrensis*** - (*Sempervivum globiferum* subsp. *tatrense*) - W. Carpathians - A form growing in acid rocks at high elevation.

J. hirta subsp. *tatrensis*

J. sobolifera (*Sempervivum globiferum* subsp. *globiferum*) - Bohemia, Poland, - Sometimes called the **Hen and Chickens Houseleek**. <u>Photo: Page 3</u>. The rosettes are open and have many short leaves. Green flushed with brownish red.

J. sobolifera

43

J. heuffelii (*Sempervivum heuffelii*) - Southern Carpathians and Balkans - Plants of this species are very distinctive. They grow into tight clusters of rosettes as the succulent stem divides. Leaves are quite rigid and generally have sharply pointed tips. A very variable species. Geographical forms differ in shape, size, colour and degree of pubescence.

- var. **heuffelii** - The 'Type' plant has greyish green leaves shading to brownish red and covered with fine hairs.
- var. **glabrum** - Rosette leaves lack hairs. Most of the geographical forms have green or greyish green leaves but they are quite distinct from each other. Geographical forms in cultivation include clones collected from Anabakanak, Anthoborio, Bakovo, Hiala, Jakupica, Kosovo, Ljubotin, Osl Jak, Ostrovika, Pasina Glava, Rhodope Mts, Treska Gorge, Uran E Vogel and Vitse.

J. heuffelii var. *heuffelii*   *J. heuffelii* var. *glabrum*

- var. **kopaonikense** - Serbia - Bright green with dark brownish-red leaf tips, pubescent leaves.

J. heuffelii var. *kopaonikense*

Interspecific hybrids

As with *Sempervivum*, most of the *Jovibarba* species will hybridise although this is rare in the wild. In cultivation each of the other *Jovibarba* species have been crossed with *J. heuffelii* and their hybrids named.

J. ×kwediana (*J. allionii* × *J. heuffelii*)
J. ×mitchelii (*J. arenaria* × *J. heuffelii*)
J. ×nixonii (*J. sobolifera* × *J. heuffelii*)
J. ×smithii (*J. hirta* × *J. heuffelii*)

J. allionii × **hirta** - An interesting hybrid that shows characteristics that are intermediate between the two parents.

Jovibarba allionii × *hirta*

Jovibarba cultivars

There are many different cultivars of *Jovibarba heuffelii* but only a relatively small number of cultivars related to the other *Jovibarba* species. A few of these are listed below and the *J. heuffelii* cultivars will be dealt with separately.

J. allionii × *hirta* '**Oki**' - This cultivar is larger and more brightly coloured than the normal hybrid. The leaves are yellowish green but with sharply contrasting dark leaf tips.

J. hirta × *sobolifera* '**Emerald Spring**' - Small, brightly coloured rosettes. Yellowish-green leaves with dark tips.

J. sobolifera '**August Cream**' - Small, pale yellowish green rosettes.

J. sobolifera '**Green Globe**' - Small rounded rosettes, leaves completely pale green.

44

Jovibarba heuffelii cultivars

Introduction

There are several hundred named cultivars of Jovibarba heuffelii and they are deservedly becoming very popular with enthusiasts.

The rosettes are much sturdier than those of *Sempervivum* cultivars. The leaves are quite rigid, usually sharply pointed and often outlined with a pale margin or silvery hairs. They come in a wide range of bright and subtle colours and although the colours may change through the seasons they generally look good all the year round.

Jovibarba heuffelii cultivars

J. heuffelii 'Iuno'
Rosette just beginning to split

They do not produce offsets on stolons, but instead the rosettes split into two or more growing points that remain attached to a common stem or caudex. This means that the groups of rosettes remain attached to each other and can eventually grow into a very impressive clump.

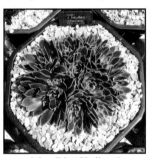

J. heuffelii 'Gladiator'
A large clump in July

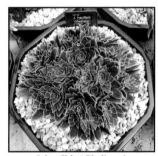

J. heuffelii 'Gladiator'
The same clump in September

Rosettes are monocarpic so after flowering, the growing point dies. This does not usually leave a gap in the clump because the other rosettes grow to fill the space.

With increasing age, the caudex does tend to break up into smaller sections and a large clump can sometimes fall to pieces as it is re-potted. There is also an increased chance of rotting off as the clump gets bigger and the older parts begin to die off.

The cultural requirements for *J. heuffelii* are the same as for *Sempervivum* cultivars. They like a well drained soil, plenty of sunlight and they will benefit from protection against too much rain in the winter. They are quite happy in the same type of compost as sempervivums.

Propagation is more difficult because individual plant groups must be dug up and cut apart to get new plants. During the growing season from spring till autumn, any rosette that has divided into two or more growing points can be cut vertically into several pieces using a sharp knife. Most of the roots will probably be lost but each piece that has a section of the stem and growing point will develop new roots and grow into a separate plant. The process of cutting into the stem exposes the living tissue to possible infection. As a precaution, the cut surfaces can be dusted with sulphur although it is usually sufficient just to leave the cuttings unplanted for a few days until the cut surface has dried. They can then be potted up as for normal offsets.

A selection of Jovibarba heuffelii cultivars

'Apache' - US - Wide green leaves with dark tips. The young leaves are pubescent.

'Apache'

'Aquarius' - UK - Large attractive cultivar with mottled blue-green and pinkish-brown leaves.

'Aquarius'

'Be Mine' - UK - Very dark blackish-red rosettes that keep good colour all the year round. The dark leaves contrast very well with the yellow flowers.

'Be Mine'

'Beacon Hill' - UK - A large-growing and beautiful cultivar. The shapely leaves are various shades of, green and red-brown.

'Beacon Hill'

'Capricorn' - UK - Interesting mottled shades of greyish-purple shading to green.

'Capricorn'

'Cherry Glow' - UK - Short leaved, tight rosettes of dark, glowing red and brown. The leaves have a fine pubescence.

'Cherry Glow'

'Copper King' - UK - Very dark brown, almost black rosettes. The leaves are outlined with tiny cilia.

'Copper King'

'Elmo's Fire' - NL - Large leaved rosettes of dark, glowing mahogany red, beautifully outlined with gold margins.

'Elmo's Fire'

'Fandango' - US - Large upright green leaves shading to dark red at the tips. The rosettes almost seem to glow in the spring.

'Fandango'

'Gladiator' - NL - Long leaved rosettes, green in the centre and shading to pinkish-brown. <u>Photos: Page 45</u>

'Greenland' - UK - The leaves are mainly green but the outer ones flush with brown or orange in the summer.

'Greenland'

'Harmony' - NL - Medium size rosettes with many leaves. The leaves are purplish-red with pale outlines.

'Harmony'

'Hotlips' - UK - Plain dark purplish-red leaves with sharply pointed tips. Rather flat rosettes.

'Hotlips'

'Iuno' - NL - Rich dark brownish-purple with pale green leaf margins. Photo: Page 45

'Jade' - UK - The leaves are shapely, and a uniform jade green colour all through the year. One of the best green cultivars.

'Jade'

'Lucky Bell' - NL - Longer and more upright leaves that are bright green shading to brown tips.

'Lucky Bell'

'Melanoheuff' - US - Very dark brownish-red leaves that appear almost black at times. The contrasting pale margins neatly outline the dark leaves

'Melanoheuff'

'Miller's Violet' - UK - Dark violet brown leaves with pale green leaf bases.

'Miller's Violet'

'Mont Rose' - NL - A lovely cultivar whose leaves shade from green to reddish-orange at the tips.

'Mont Rose'

'Mink' - UK - Dark purplish-red leaves that are covered with a fine pubescence.

'Mink'

'Minuta' - UK - A form with very small, densly clustering green rosettes.

'Minuta'

'Mystique' - 'US - Short wide leaves. In the spring the leaves are green at the base shading to dark brownish-red tips. The colour darkens through the summer to a rich purplish-red.

'Mystique' - March

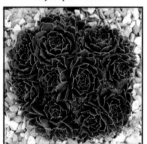

'Mystique' - October

'Nanette' - UK - Pale bluish-green flushed with greyish purple in the summer.

'Nannette'

'Orion' - UK - Large rosettes of wide glossy leaves that go completely dark red in the summer.

'Orion' - April

'Orion' - October

'Pellister' - ? - This is a beautiful clone but it could be a collected form from Mt Pelister, Macedonia rather than a cultivar.

'Pellister'

'Prisma' - UK - A small-growing cultivar. Bright green leaves with dark brown tips in the spring.

'Prisma'

'Pyrope' - NL - Dark blackish-purple leaves with silver margins. The leaves are wide and the rosettes are very symmetrical.

'Pyrope'

'Serenade' - NL - Large rosettes. Golden brown leaves turning to intense red in the summer.

'Serenade'

'Springael's Choice' - BE - One of the largest growing cultivars. The rosettes are flat and wide and the leaves shade from yellowish green at the base to dark brownish-red tips.

'Springael's Choice'

'**Suntan**' - UK - Large wide leaves in shades of golden brown and green, outlined with cream edges.

'Suntan'

'**Tan**' - UK - Beautiful dark red-brown leaves in the summer but rather slow growing.

'Tan'

'**Tancredi**' - UK - Wide, rather flat rosettes with many leaves. The colour of each leaf shades from bluish-green to greyish purple. This is another slow-growing cultivar.

'Tancredi'

'**Toronto**' - UK - Dark blackish-red leaves in the spring.These turn a rich dark red in the summer.

'Toronto'

'**Tuxedo**' - UK - The rosettes are golden brown in the spring but turn to dark purplish-grey in the summer and autumn.

'Tuxedo' - April

'Tuxedo'- October

'**Vesta**' - NL - Wide flat rosettes with many, rather short leaves. These are dark brownish-purple with pale edges, producing a neat checker-board effect.

'Vesta'

'**Xanthoheuff**' - US - The rosettes are bright yellow in the spring but gradually become more green as summer arrives. By the autumn it is almost all green but the outer leaves are often flushed with orange. One of the most spectacular cultivars but it is prone to rotting off before turning green.

'Xanthoheuff' - March

'**Zembla**' - NL - Glossy, rich brownish-purple leaves with pale margins.

'Zembla'

49

Further information

Sempervivums are often mentioned in general books on alpines, rock gardens, or cacti and succulents but there are very few books that deal specifically with them. The most comprehensive sources of information are now found on the Internet.

Gérard Dumont's website (http://sempervivophilia.free.fr/) is the best source of information for anyone seriously interested in *Sempervivum* and *Jovibarba*. The author concentrates on naturally occurring species but also provides detailed information on all aspects of *Sempervivum* study. The text is mainly in French but many parts have been translated into English. Even those who cannot read French will gain a huge amount of information from this excellent site. There is also a comprehensive bibliography that can be downloaded and a large collection of photographs of plants in their natural habitats. The site also has the latest version of Martin Miklanek's list of cultivars.

When looking for information it is probably best to use one of the Internet search engines to find what is currently available. New websites are constantly being set up and some of these contain large numbers of photgraphs of sempervivums. Most of them also provide links to other relevant websites.

Our own website (http://www.fernwood-nursery.co.uk) gives more information about our collections and provides links to some other sites of interest.

Other publications

There are a few publications devoted to sempervivums but most are currently out of print. Some can occasionally be found in second hand bookshops and many are downloadable for private study from Gérard Dumont's website. Some publications in English that we have found useful are listed below.

The Genus Sempervivum and Jovibarba, Alan C. Smith (1975)
> A privately published booklet containing descriptions of species and cultivars together with a useful identification key.

An Account of the Sempervivum Group, Lloyd Praeger (1932)
> A reference work for the enthusiast. The nomenclature is now out of date and the more recently discovered species are not included, but it does contain detailed descriptions, including diagrams, of all the species known at the time. It was reprinted in 1967.

Plant Jewels of the High Country, Helen E. Payne (1972)
> This hard-back book contains photographs and descriptions of a number of sempervivums and sedums. The nomenclature is out of date but it makes interesting reading and there are useful sections on the cultivation and display of plants.

Flora Europea, Cambridge University Press (1993)
> There are identification keys and descriptions of European species of *Sempervivum* and *Jovibarba* on pages 352-356.

Many other publications in various languages are referenced on Gérard Dumont's website and we would recommend this as the best starting point for any serious study.

Conclusion

We hope that this brief account of *Sempervivum* and *Jovibarba* species and cultivars will have given a good introduction to this beautiful and fascinating group of plants. We have only presented a very small sample of the plants that exist but we have tried to make it representative of the wide range of different forms that are available to enthusiasts in this country.

We hope that some questions have been answered and perhaps some problems avoided but most of all, we hope that we have been able to stimulate interest in a charming group of plants that are sometimes overlooked.

We will end with some quotes from Reginald Farrah, one of the great writers about alpines and rock garden plants. In Volume II of **The English Rock Garden** (1922), referring to sempervivums in general he states:

"They are all of the easiest culture and the loveliest effect ... green blue, violet, ruby; or of all shades commingled; or cobwebbed till they are like Ping-pong balls in cotton wool."

His descriptions of species include:

"S. calcareum is singularly beautiful with its large rosettes, which are specially ample and fat, specially neatly packed, of a lovely glaucous-blue, with an abrupt dark purple tip to each leaf."

and when describing *S. arachnoideum* ... *"It is really a lovely little jewel"* ... and its flowers ... *"twelve-rayed stars in the most glowing shade of ruby rose, shining on the hot banks of the Alps like little catherine-wheels of living red light above the crowded whiteness of the globules below."*

We cannot match the glorious language of Reginald Farrar but we certainly share his enthusiasm for the plants.

Fernwood Nursery

At Fernwood, we grow over 1200 different varieties of *Sempervivum* and *Jovibarba* and our collection is increasing all the time. It provides us with interest and pleasure all the year round. In 1998, our collections of *Sempervivum, Jovibarba* and *Rosularia* were awarded **National Collection**® status by the National Council for the Conservation of Plants & Gardens. (NCCPG).

We also hold a **National Collection**® of *Phormium* species and cultivars.

General view of the nursery area - spot the inquisitive pheasant!

At the nursery we have our National Collections® on display, and we propagate plants for sale by mail order, at plant shows and to visitors. We welcome people to view the collections or to purchase plants but we do not have regular opening times. Please telephone or email first to arrange a visit.

We normally start sending mail order plants towards the end of April and continue until the end of October, or later if weather permits. Please send a S.A.E. for our current availability list. The list can also be downloaded from our website.

http://www.fernwood-nursery.co.uk

Howard and Sally Wills
Fernwood Nursery
Peters Marland
TORRINGTON
Devon, EX38 8QG

Telephone: 01805 601446, *E-mail*: hw@fernwood-nursery.co.uk